The Life of
Riley

Why am I so big?

By Sharron Watson
Karen Martin

Illustrated by Karen Martin

To order additional copies of this book, contact:
Xlibris Corporation
1-888-795-4274
www.Xlibris.com
Orders@Xlibris.com

Dedicated to Robert and Virginia Wright who
always believed in us.
For Riley, a life of inspiration.

My name is Riley. I am an Irish Wolfhound. Dogs like me have been around a long time, but we are rare to see. My family knows I am special because they always say, "Oh, Riley!" But why am I so big?

I don't like to swim, but as a puppy I loved my bath. Everyone had fun chasing me around the house calling, "Oh, Riley!" Sometimes furniture was in my way.

Why am I so big?

When I was a puppy, I liked to follow my master to the barn. River lives there. He is even bigger than I am. One day I tried to play with River. He kicked me out of the way! "Oh, Riley," my master said. Now I cannot fit under the fence to visit River.
Why am I so big?

Rosie shows me how to be a good dog in a people house. She curls up by the fireplace. There is not much room there for me. Her food is in a little dish on the floor, but mine sits up on a stand. I just check to see if her food is good. "Oh, Riley leave Rosie's dish alone."

Why am I so big?

I have good eyes to discover new things outdoors. The brightly colored flowers look pretty and smell sweet. The orange fish like to swim, but not me. Butterflies fly in the garden, but I can't. I chase the cat under the bushes, but I get stuck. I hear, "Oh, Riley!" Why am I so big?

I have my own bed, but I like the one where my master sleeps the best. Sometimes it gets too crowded. They say, "Oh, Riley!"
Why am I so big?

Sometimes I go for rides in a car. My master calls, "Oh, Riley let's go." When it is sunny I ride in the special car without a roof. What a view I have! I like to feel the wind. People often stare. I don't know why. I just sit up tall.

Why am I so big?

I went to school with other dogs. They were smaller and could do tricks. The teacher said I was smart. The school gave me a special scarf when I learned my lessons. Owners with the other dogs looked at me, "Oh, Riley you are huge."

Why am I so big?

With my special scarf I get to visit places where other dogs can't.
I like to go to the library where children sit with books. They
read to me. Kids lean on me and hug me like a stuffed animal.
Someone whispers, "Oh, Riley you are my friend."
Is this why I am so big?

I like to wear my special scarf to the hospital. At school I learned how to act around people. Some people in the hospital can't get out of bed, so I put my head right next to theirs. Others have special chairs. We can see eye to eye. The people smile, pet me, and say "Oh, Riley you made my day!"

Is this why I am so big?

Our family has special days when they open packages, find candy, or dress in funny or scary clothes. But my favorite special day is when everyone dresses in green. I wear my special scarf and a hat. Soon I see other dogs like me. We get to lead the St. Patrick's Day Parade. All the people gather and cheer, "Oh, Riley you are beautiful!"

Is this why I am so big?

"Oh, Riley," I think, "I am a special dog who helps people. I make them happy. I am proud to be an Irish Wolfhound!"

"That is why I am so big!"

The Irish Wolfhound

The Irish Wolfhound (Cu´ Faoil in Irish) is an ancient breed of domestic dog. Roman records dated 391 AD describe these galloping hounds as war dogs, guards, and hunters. The Celts bred these sighthounds as war dogs over two thousand years ago. Using its sight, intelligence, size, and speed the Wolfhound was very good at pulling men from chariots as well as hunting wolves and boar. One Irish proverb describes the dog as "Gentle when stroked, fierce when provoked."

As a symbol of Celtic people many poems and stories were written about them. One story includes Patrick McAlpern, better known as St. Patrick. In exchange for caring for some Wolfhounds, Patrick was given passage to the European continent. The crew and animals were near starvation when they arrived, but were saved when the hounds hunted food after Patrick prayed.

Due to their size and intelligence Irish Wolfhounds are considered a "king of dogs". In fact this breed was the companion of kings. During the Middle Ages only royalty could legally own them. Wolfhounds became very valuable as gifts to nobility outside of Ireland, contributing to their near extinction. In 1652 a Declaration was issued to ban their exportation. Major H.D. Richardson is credited with beginning to save the breed in the early 1800s. Captain George Augustus Graham continued the efforts to save the Wolfhound, breeding and writing about them in the late 1800s. The modern Irish Wolfhound is more gentle than the ancient breed since it was no longer bred for attacking or hunting. However, the breed still has traits of hunting dogs.

Today the average Wolfhound stands approximately 36 inches tall, and weighs up to 180 pounds. They have rough hair ranging from cream to black. Grey shades are the most recognizable. These patient dogs are loving companions for many families.

Riley's gentle nature and intelligence makes her a good therapy dog. Therapy dogs are working dogs trained to visit patients in hospitals and residents in nursing facilities. These dogs have extensive training in order to be certified as a therapy dog. Training alone does not make a good therapy dog. The animal needs to be gentle, obedient, social, and polite. Riley is a successful therapy dog due to her calm, yet friendly personality. Therapy Dogs International (TDI) is the organization in which she is certified. Riley lives with her family in Ohio.

Sources:
www.irishwolfhounds.org
www.wikipedia.org
The Intelligence of Dogs by Stanley Coren
Research done by Sharon Watson

Critical Thinking

- Share a time when you were told you were too big or too small to do something others were doing.
- What books would you read with Riley? How would you feel sitting with Riley?
- What do you think makes Riley a good visiting dog?
- If you were a visiting dog, where would you go? Why?
- Describe what makes you special.

Sharron Watson has been an elementary teacher in rural Pennsylvania for over 20 years which, along with raising two daughters, inspired her to write for children. Collaborating with her sister Karen to create children's books has been a dream for many years. Sharron is currently writing a Riley sequel and a chapter book, The Adventures of Ema Lea Lynnee. Reading, playing in a bell choir, and walking along Sunset Beach, North Carolina are her favorite past-times.

Karen Martin has been a watercolor artist for many years, and now is exploring the world of illustrations. Working with her sister Sharron for the illustrations on the sequel to Riley as well has other upcoming books has been a lifelong dream. She resides in Seville, Ohio with her husband, daughters and stepsons, and loves to spend her days among her horses, dogs, cats, and Koi. The experiences with her Irish Wolfhound, Riley, has brought so much joy into her life and sharing her with the world has been rewarding. Visit karenmartinart.com

Edwards Brothers,Inc!
Thorofare, NJ 08086
16 June, 2010
BA2010167